CW00350898

Educational Consultant: Betty Root

Betty Root has a lifetime of experience in education, as a teacher, lecturer and consultant. She has written, or acted as advisor on, numerous books for primary and pre-school children.

First published in Great Britain 1998 by Egmont UK Limited,
This edition published 2008 by Dean, an imprint of Egmont UK Limited,
239 Kensington High Street, London W8 6SA

HiT entertainment

Thomas the Tank Engine & Friends™

CREATED BY BRITT ALLCROFT

Based on The Railway Series by The Reverend W Awdry

ISBN 978 0 6035 6267 9
5 7 9 10 8 6 4
Printed in Italy

Match the things that are the same.

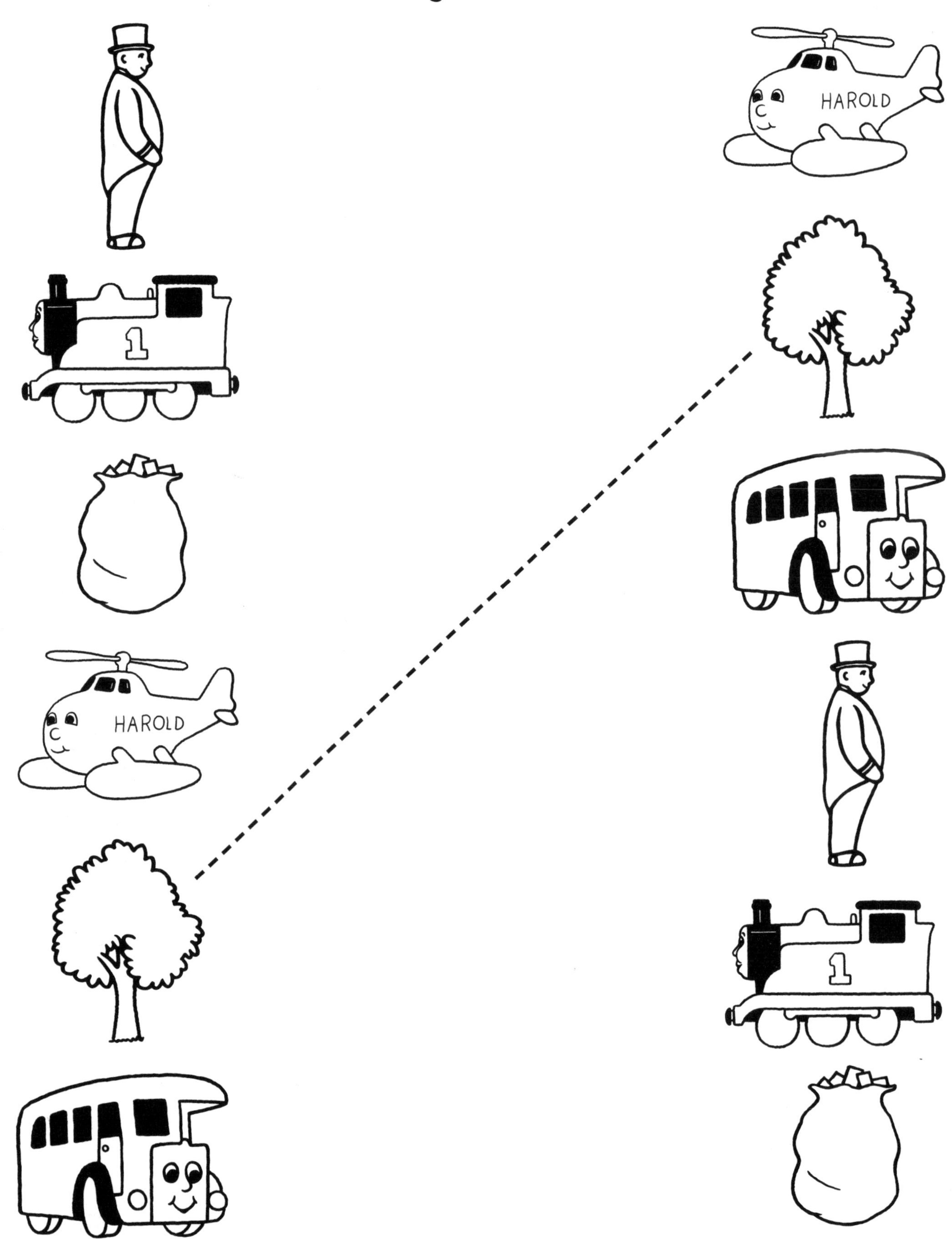

Put a cross through the odd one out.

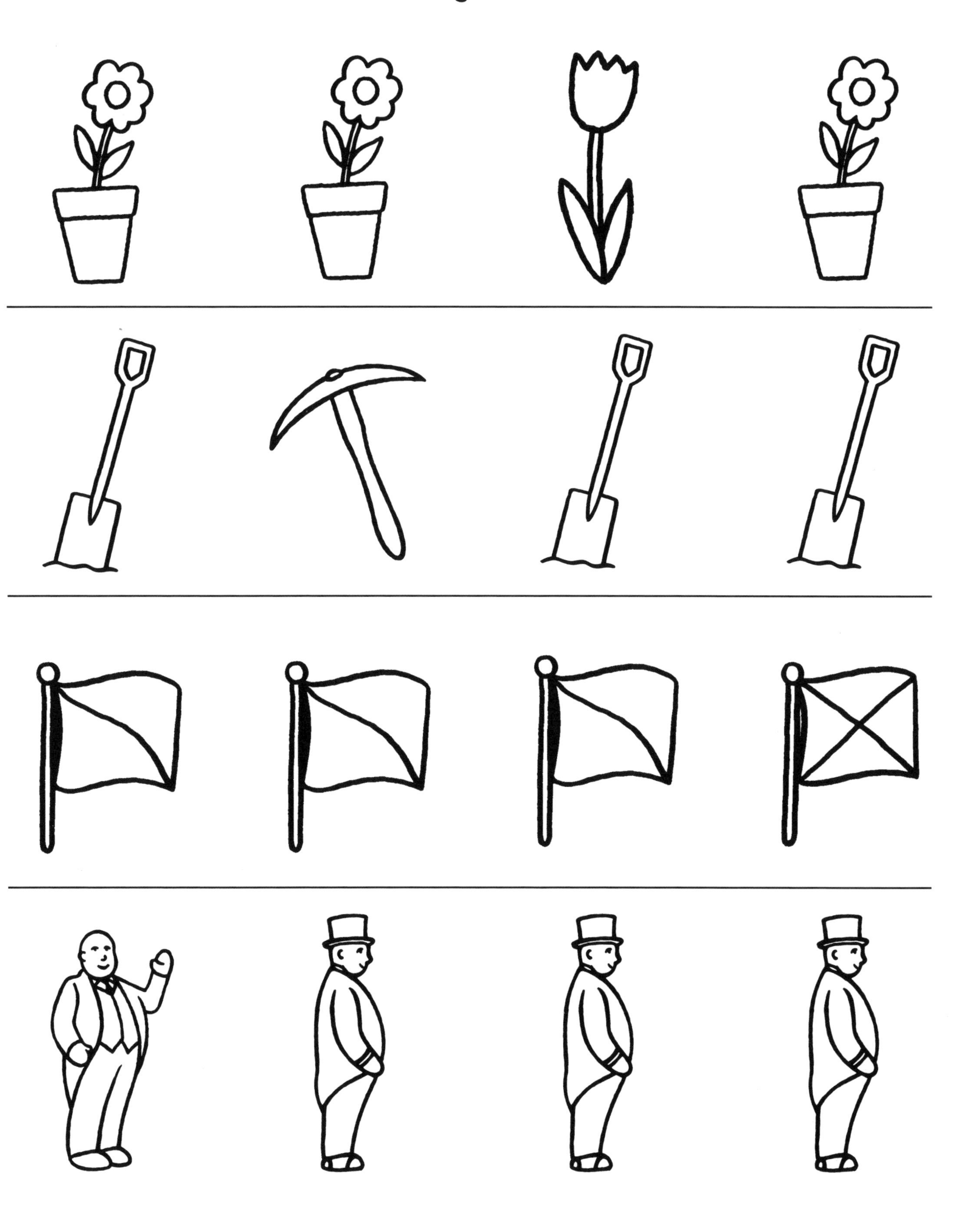

Match the things that belong together.

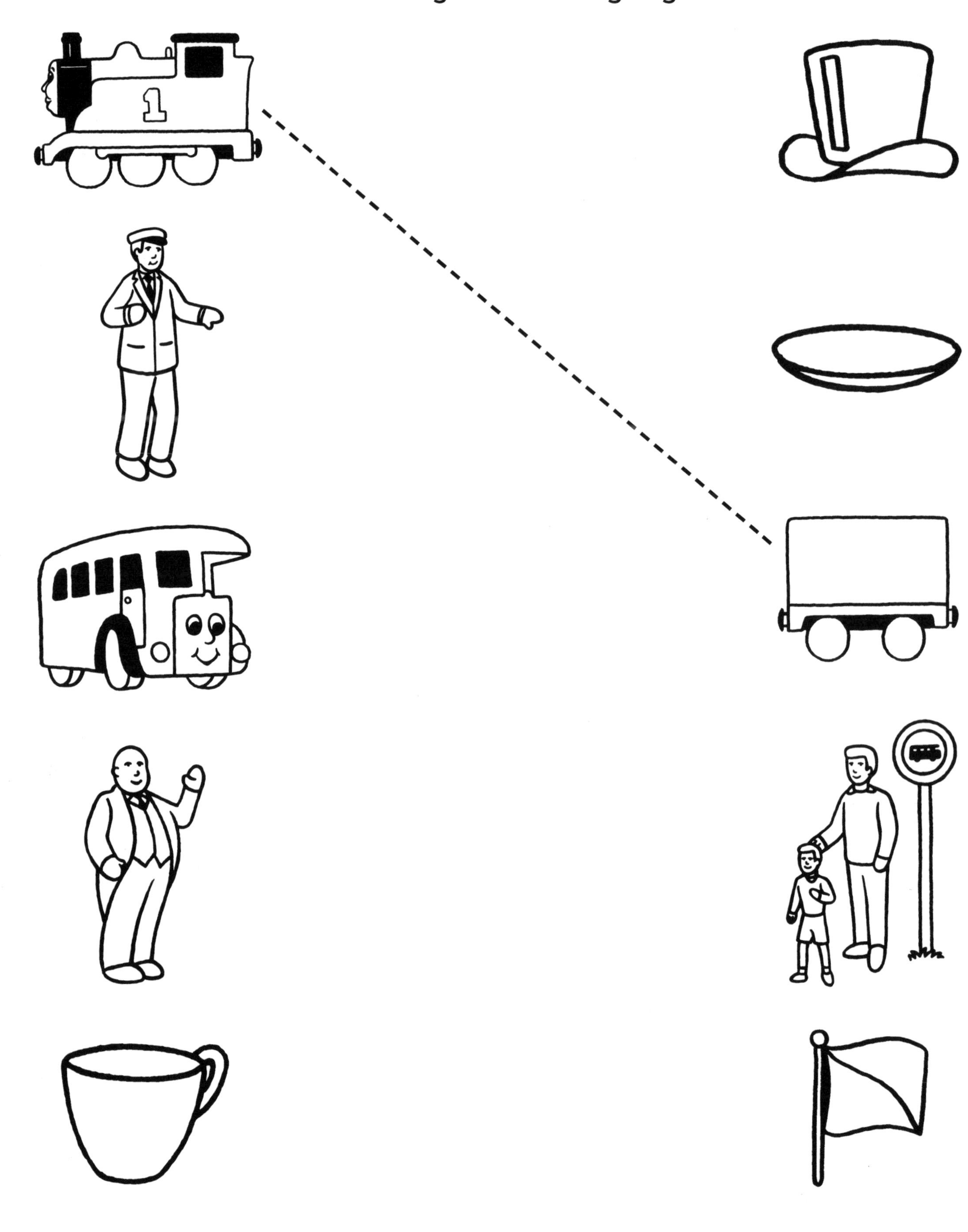

Colour the things which you can see in the big picture below.

Draw a yellow circle round each letter **s**.

sun

Draw a blue circle around each letter **e**.

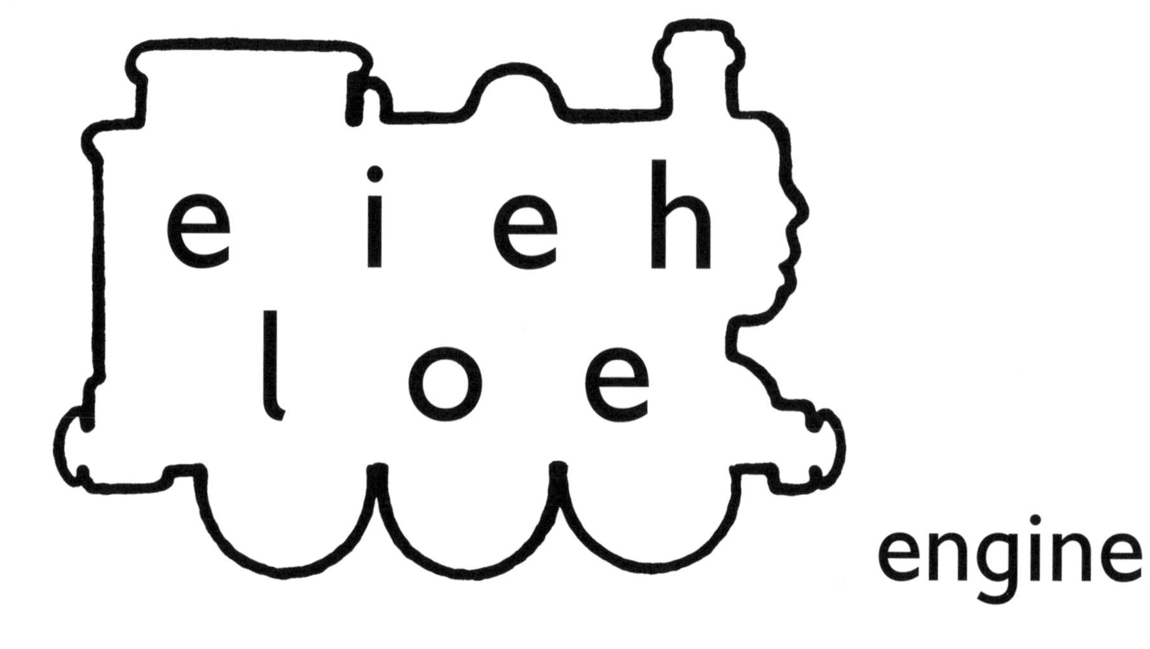

engine

Put a cross through the odd one out.

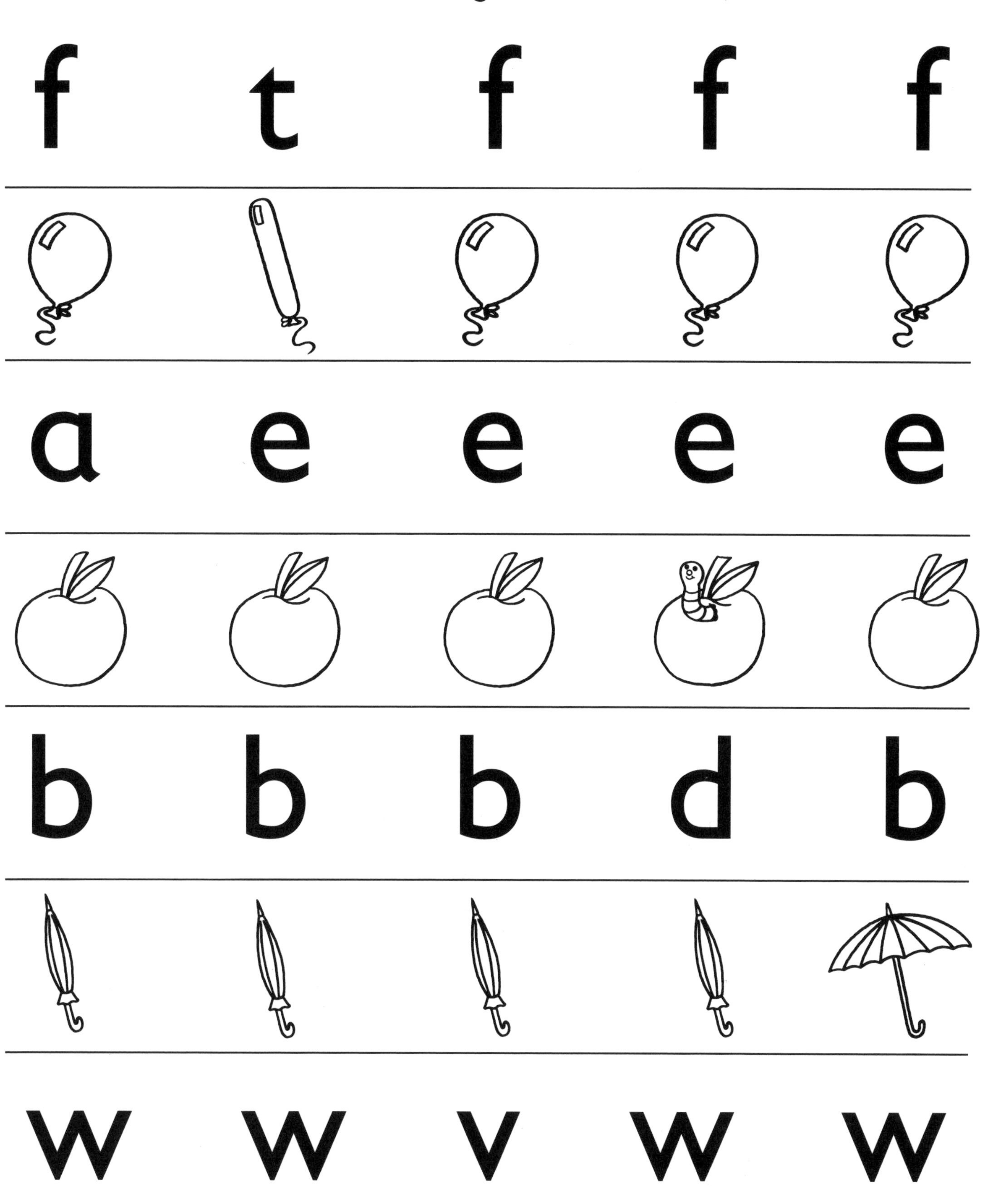

Draw a red circle around each letter h.

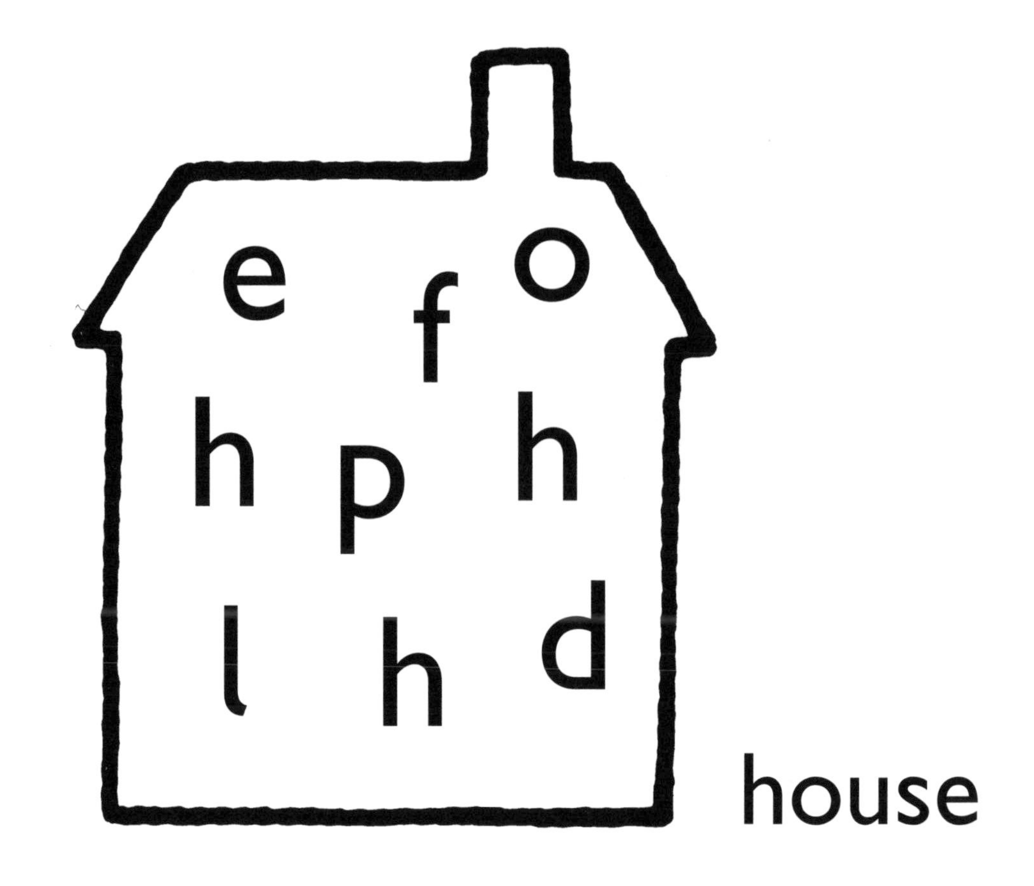

Draw a blue circle around each letter f.

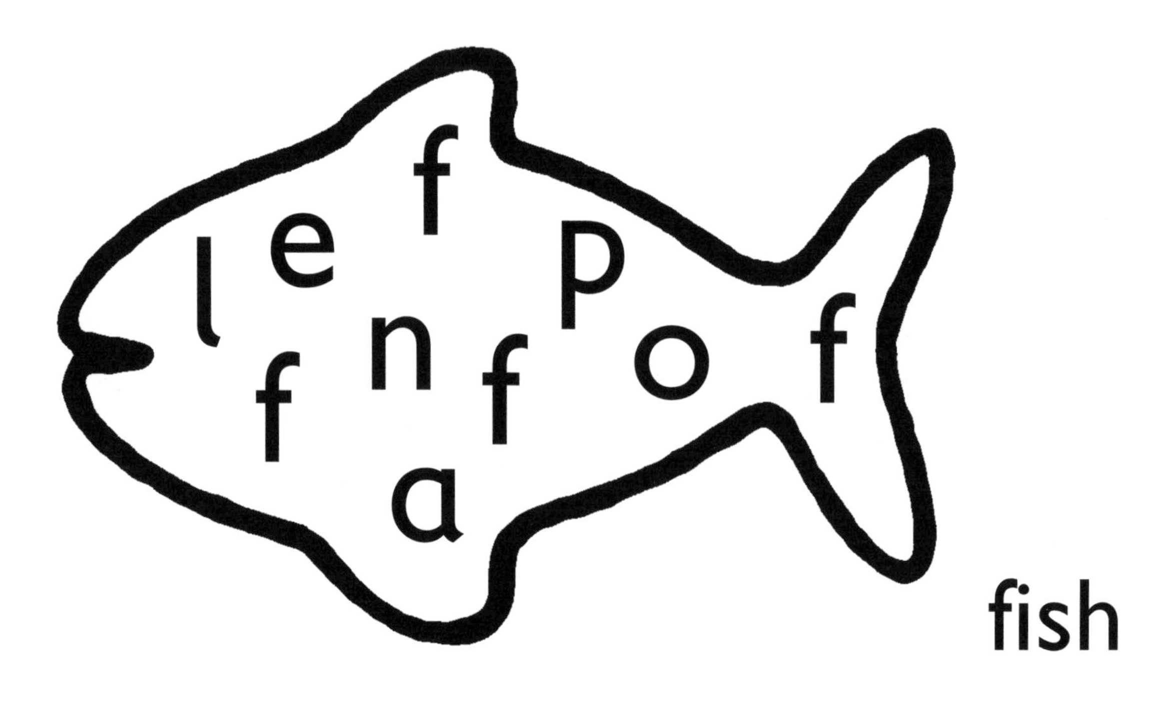

Look at the top picture. Now look at the bottom picture and find the 7 differences. Circle them.

Look at the pictures and tell a story.

Now draw what happens next.

Join two letters which are the same.

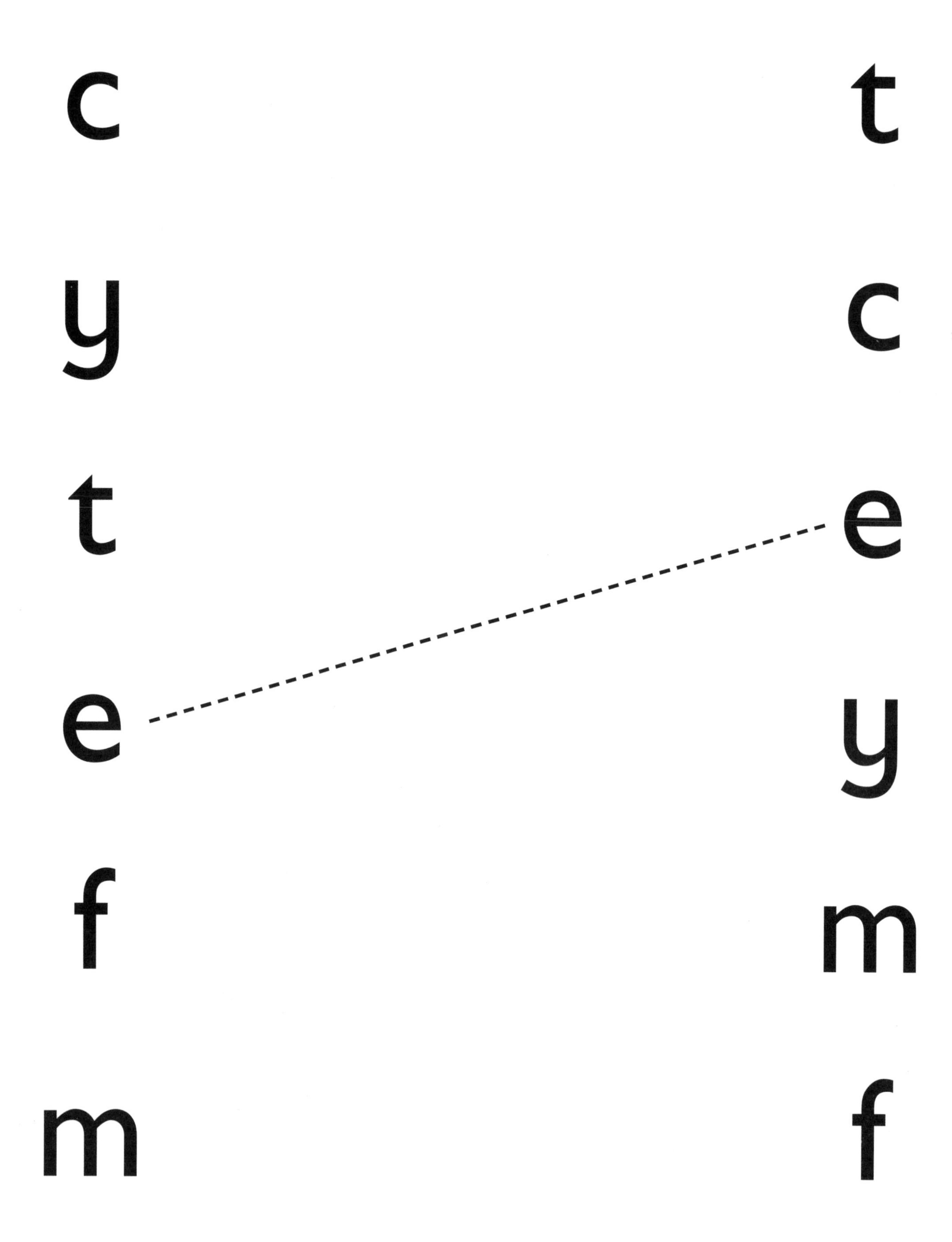

Percy is pushing trucks at the mine.

What happens next? Choose the right ending and colour it in.

Thomas' Driver is eating his lunch.

Which of these were in his lunch box? Colour them.

cake

sandwich

pie

apple

banana

carrot

Draw a red circle round each letter **a**.

Draw a yellow circle round each letter **b**.

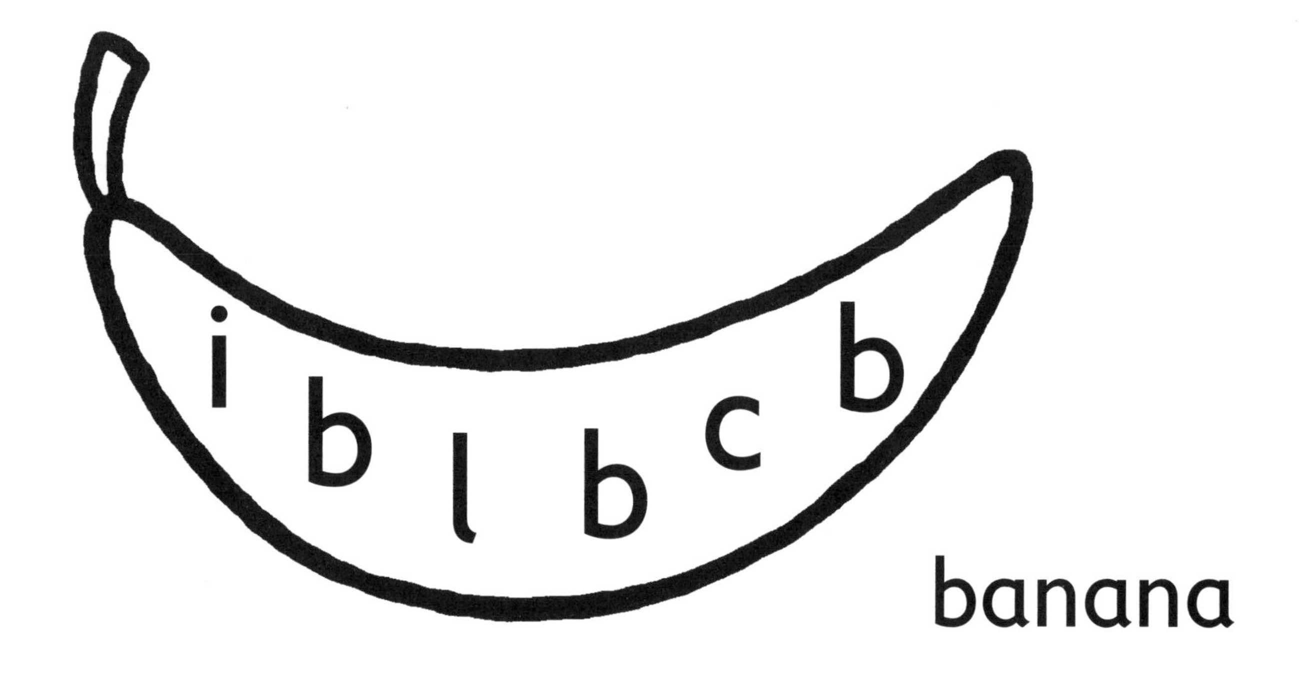

Join two letters which are the same.

Tell the story in the pictures and draw what happens next.

The station cat is missing. Can you find him in each picture?

"Where is the cat?" says The Fat Controller.

"Where is the cat?" says Thomas' Driver.

"Where is the cat?" say Thomas' passengers.

Thomas knows where the cat is. Do you?

Draw a blue circle round each letter **c**.

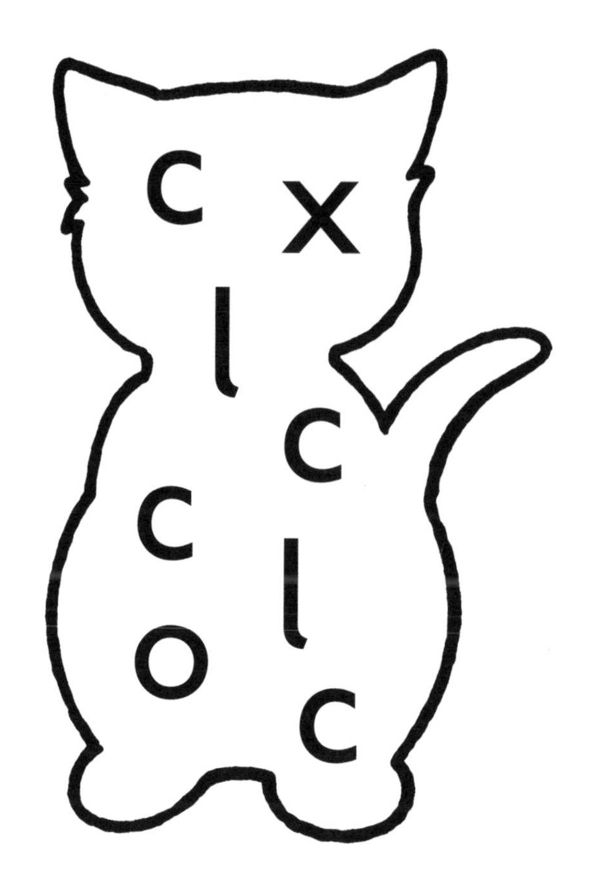

cat

Draw an orange circle round each letter **d**.

duck

Match the pictures to the letter sounds.

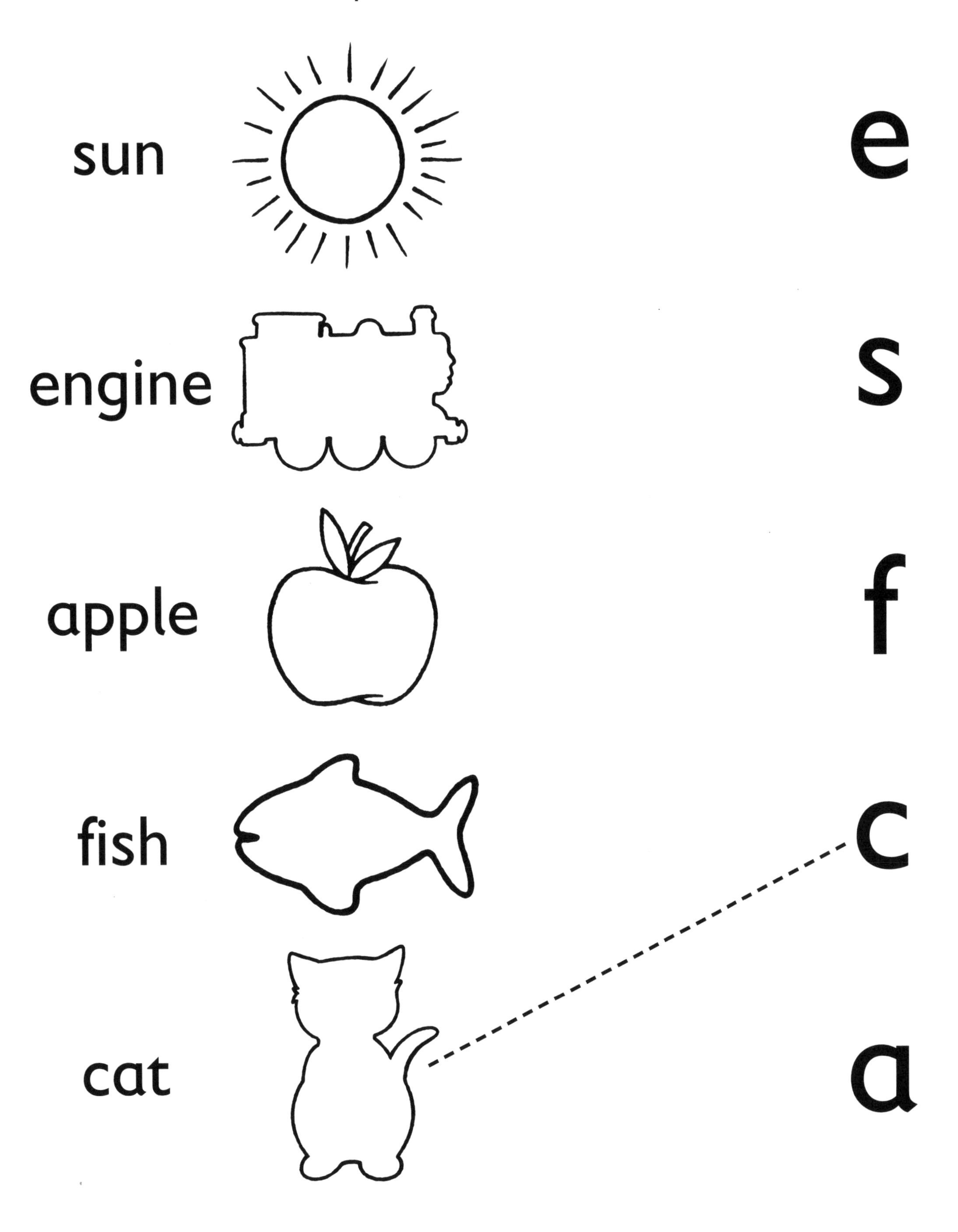

Colour in the picture below.

g - green b - blue
y - yellow r - red

Look carefully at this picture. There are six letters hidden in it.
Find them and write them in the space below.

__________________ __________________

__________________ __________________

__________________ __________________

FIRST READING

This book is part of a series designed to prepare children for starting school. The following skills are covered in this book:

- looking at pictures carefully
- story-telling
- recognising some simple letter shapes
- connecting these letters with the sounds they represent

The aim at this stage is to build confidence and make learning as much fun as possible. By working on these activities with your child, you can offer help and encouragement, and share the fun. Here are a few simple ways that you can help your child to learn.

- Start at the beginning of the book and work through each page. The activities get gradually more difficult, building on what your child has learnt.
- Short sessions are more likely to hold your child's interest, so do not try to do too much in one go. You might start with just one activity. Stop if your child is losing concentration or an activity seems too difficult: you can always come back to it later.
- Be sure to reward your child's efforts. If your child feels successful, they will be keen to learn next time.
- Discuss each activity with your child to make certain that it is understood before any writing takes place. Asking questions and puzzling out the activities together is an important part of the learning process.
- Where letters are used in an activity, encourage your child to say the letter names and the sounds aloud.
- Talk about the pictures together. Discuss what might happen in the stories.